The
Many Shades
of
GENDER

Adult Coloring Book

Inspiring Designs and Affirmations
Connecting All Identities

by
Ronald Holt and
William Huggett

he Many Shades of Gender Adult Coloring Book is a celebration of all gender iden-
ties. Each person has unique characteristics that contribute to the vibrant mosaic of
umanity.

/e hope you find the content helpful. We invite all people who are open to messages of
ve, hope, inspiration, and healing.

/herever you are on the gender spectrum, we stand with you. We are united and wel-
ɔme one another. Unity, strength, and healing come when we embrace diversity.

his coloring book is intended to bring hope and encouragement to everyone, as we
nbrace the identities that make each of us beautiful and unique.

ɔ as you go into the stillness of coloring, we encourage you to enter into whatever
rocess allows your deeper self to emerge. We invite you to grow and expand into the
eautiful, authentic person that only you can be.

ɔu are worthy of unconditional love and acceptance – just the way you are.

ɔ get more information about Dr. Holt, his speaking engagements, other books or vid-
ɔs, please visit DrRonHolt.com. You can find more information about Dr. Huggett at
/illiamHuggett.com.

incerely-

I am beautiful in so many ways.

GENER

sexuality

status   queer

INTERSECTIONAL

immigrant   ethnicity

multicultural

IDENTITY

I am human.
I have many dimensions.
I am beautiful.

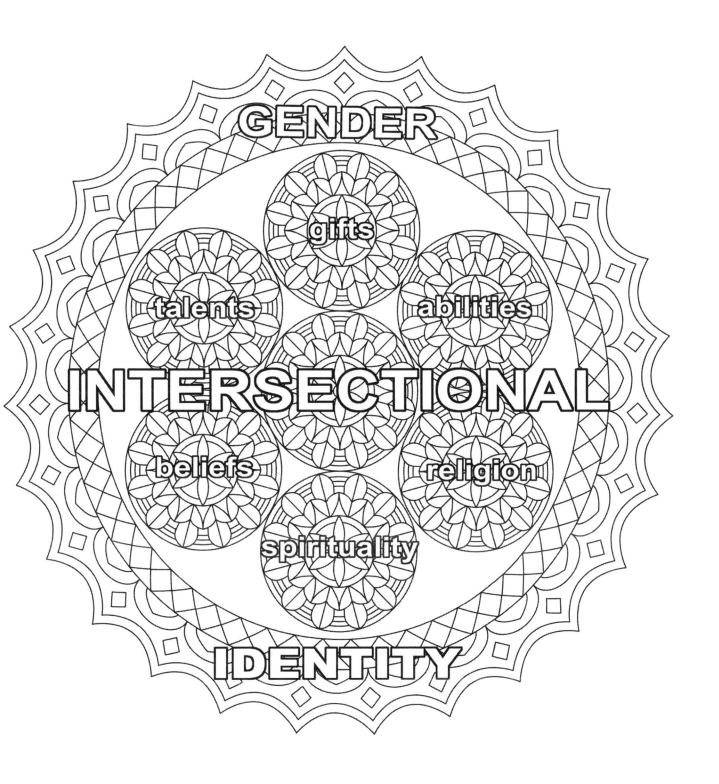

I am the authority on
my identity and expression.

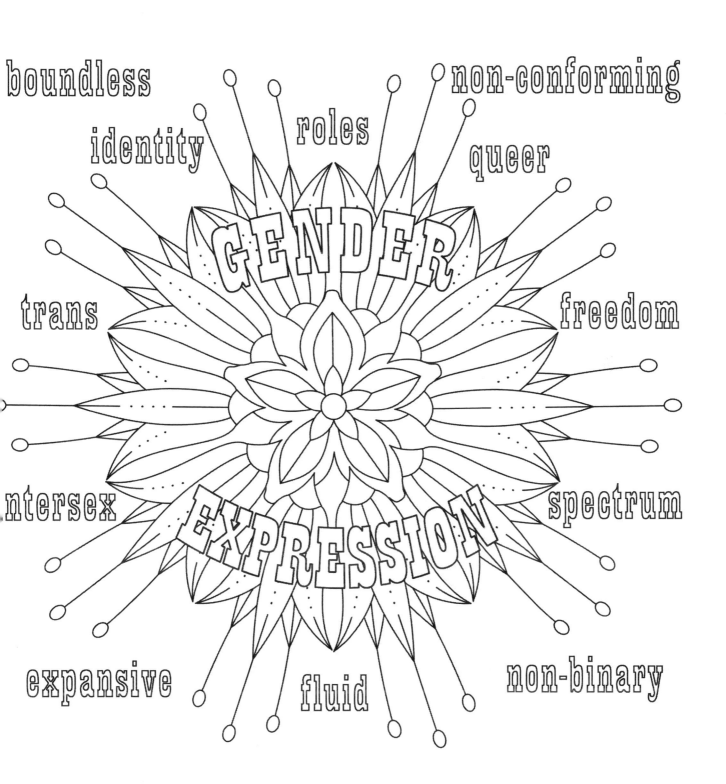

boundless

identity

roles

non-conforming

queer

GENDER

trans

freedom

intersex

EXPRESSION

spectrum

expansive

fluid

non-binary

Unlimited love for others
starts by loving myself.

I deserve to feel safe
in all areas of my life.

SAFE PLACES

government community home family public space friends work school

We're not asking for special rights --
just human rights.

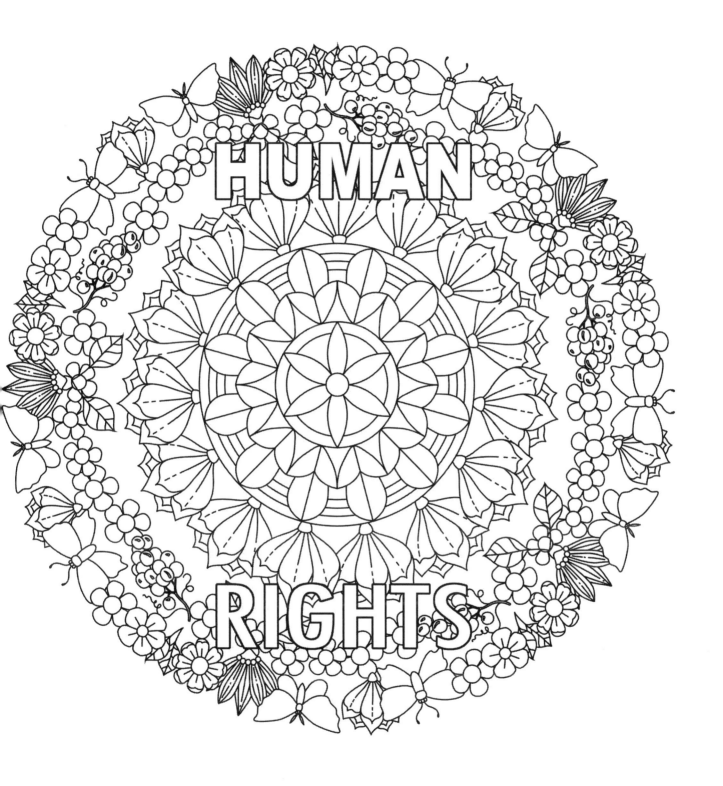

No matter how I identify, I belong.

transmasculine

agender

non-binary

neutral

MTF

androgynous

gender queer

fluid

transfeminine

pangender

FTM

third gender

variant

I have the right and the responsibility
to be who I was born to be.

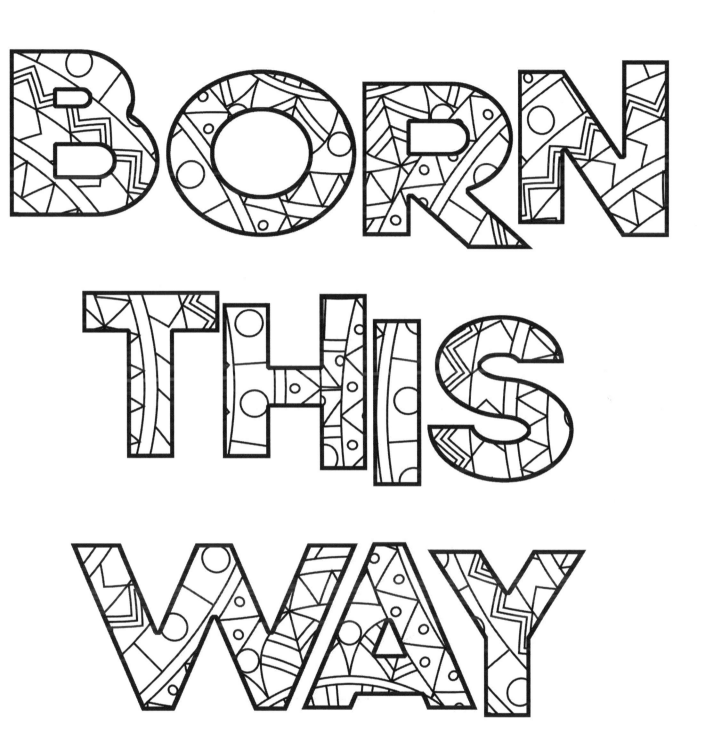

I feel best when I am
my authentic self.

My gender identity is a deep
and abiding truth within.

Together we are stronger.
Together we are one.

ALLY

STRONGER

TOGETHER

I use pronouns that feel
most natural to me.

PRONOUNS

she
her
hers

ve
ver
vis

ey
em
eirs

ze
hir
hirs

yo
yo
yos

xe
xem
xyrs

per
per
pers

he
him
his

they them theirs

27

I am fully supported in
my growth and development.
My transition is defined by me.

transitioning

coming out

medical

family

social

physical

surgical

hormonal

emotional

I am worthy of unconditional
love and acceptance --
just as I am.

My identity is valid
and I matter.

identity

validity

I take comfort knowing
others want to support me.

LEGAL

transgenderlegal.org

ACLU.org

GLAD.org

SRLP.org

transgenderlawcenter.org

NCLRights.org

RESOURCES

My health and well-being
matter. I have value.

WELLNESS

suicidepreventionlifeline.org

TheTrevorProject.org

translifeline.org

transhealth.ucsf.edu

RESOURCES

Being myself is my highest calling.
Living authentically is liberating.

I am committed to
the safety, inclusion, and
well-being of all gender identities.

INCLUSION AND

WELL

BEING

OF ALL PEOPLE

My life's journey of healing and
wholeness is unfolding before me.

WHOLENESS AUTHENTICITY

TRANSFORMATION

HEALING JOURNEY

I am not alone.
Others love and support me.

ADVOCACY

transequality.org

GLSEN.org

PFLAG.org

GSANetwork.org

HRC.org

GLAAD.org

genderspectrum.org

RESOURCES

I continue to fight everyday
for gender equality.

Love transcends all boundaries.

love
knows
no
gender

I accept others.
I embrace myself.

ACCEPT EXISTENCE

EMBRACE ACCEPTANCE

I offer unconditional love
to myself and others.

Today, I embrace and accept
the diverse and unique peson
that is me.

I am worthy and fully accept myself.

confident
loved
real

determined
grateful
valid

peaceful
strong
kind

accepted
smart

I
AM

grounded
worthy

brave
beautiful

diligent
compassionate

whole
authentic

Today I offer the world
my greatest gift --
my authentic self.

Today I commit to loving
myself for who I am.

I LOVE
MYSELF

63

Whenever someone is lifted up,
we all rise.

I work to create a world
where all people have the right
to live in peace and love.

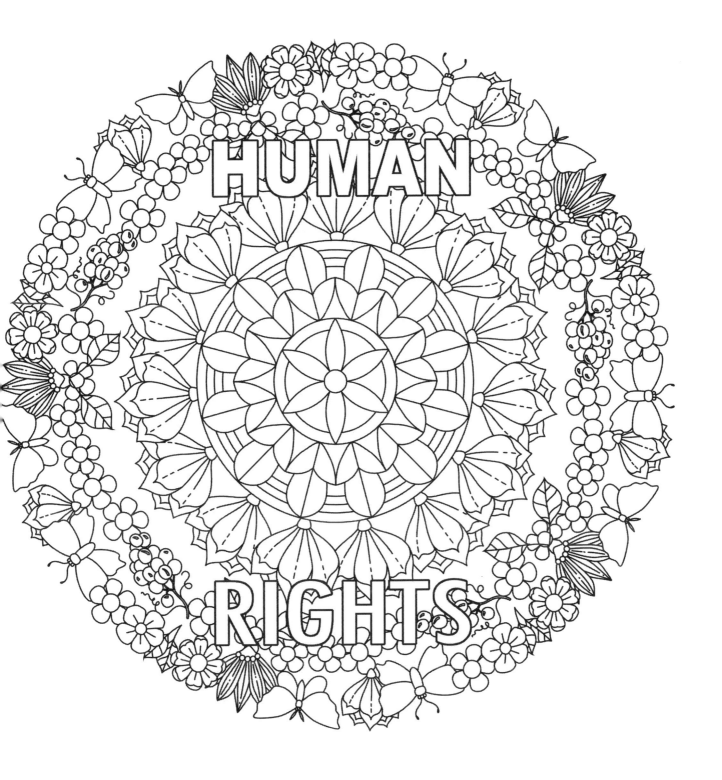

Made in the USA
Monee, IL
23 December 2019

19450100R00037